ME
AND MY
FAMILY
TREE

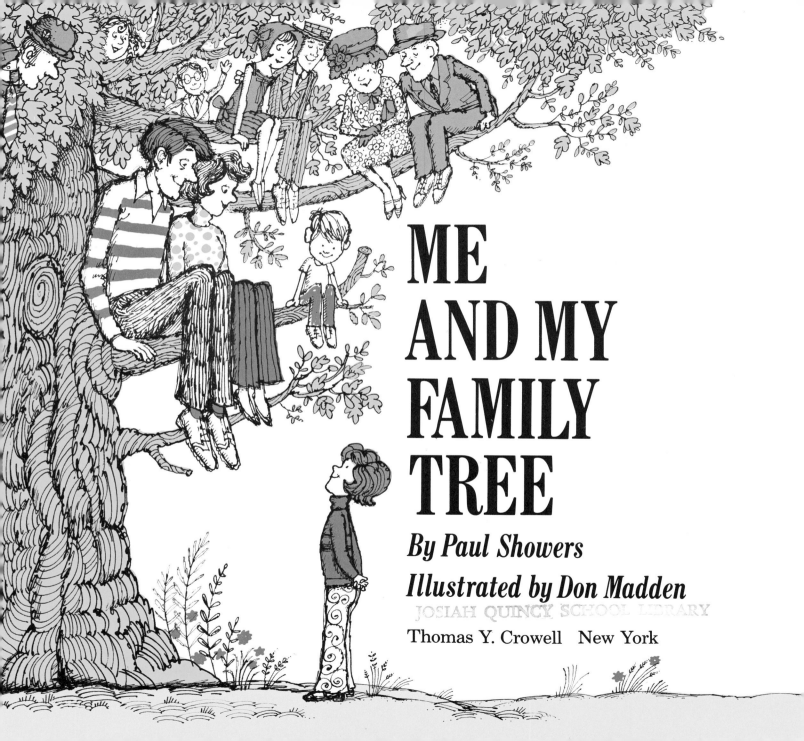

ME AND MY FAMILY TREE

By Paul Showers

Illustrated by Don Madden

Thomas Y. Crowell   New York

Other *Let's-Read-and-Find-Out Science Books* you will enjoy

A Baby Starts to Grow by Paul Showers · *Before You Were a Baby* by Paul Showers and Kay Sperry Showers · *A Drop of Blood* by Paul Showers · *Fat and Skinny* by Philip Balestrino · *Hear Your Heart* by Paul Showers · *How Many Teeth?* by Paul Showers · *How You Talk* by Paul Showers · *Look at Your Eyes* by Paul Showers · *The Skeleton Inside You* by Philip Balestrino · *Straight Hair, Curly Hair* by Augusta Goldin · *Use Your Brain* by Paul Showers · *Your Skin and Mine* by Paul Showers

Let's-Read-and-Find-Out Science Books are edited by Dr. Roma Gans, Professor Emeritus of Childhood Education, Teachers College, Columbia University, and Dr. Franklyn M. Branley, Astronomer Emeritus and former Chairman of The American Museum-Hayden Planetarium. For a complete catalog of *Let's-Read-and-Find-Out Science Books,* write to Thomas Y. Crowell, Department 363, 10 East 53rd Street, New York, New York 10022.

Library of Congress Cataloging in Publication Data
Showers, Paul. Me and my family tree. (Let's-read-and-find-out books)
SUMMARY: Briefly discusses the principles of genetics and heredity as illustrated by a youngster's family tree.
1. Genetics—Juvenile literature. (1. Heredity. 2. Genetics) I. Madden, Don. II. Title.
QH437.5.856 1978   575.1   77-26595   ISBN 0-690-03886-0   ISBN 0-690-03887-9 lib. bdg.

FIRST EDITION

ME
AND MY
FAMILY
TREE

I have a great big family. I have a mother and a father and a little brother. My mother isn't tall like my father. She can't reach dishes on the top shelf—but my father can. My father has red hair. I do, too.

I have my parents, my brother, and me. But my family is bigger than that.

My mother and father have sisters and brothers. They
are my aunts and uncles. Their children are my cousins.
But my family is bigger than that.

My mother has a mother and father. They are my
grandmother and grandfather. Grandmother is like my
mother—she isn't very tall.

I have another grandmother and grandfather. They
are my father's parents. That gives me four grandparents
in my family. But my family is bigger than that.

Each one of my grandmothers had a mother and father. Each one of my grandfathers had a mother and father, too.

my great~grandparents on Mother's side

That gives me four great-grandmothers and four great-grandfathers. Eight great-grandparents in my family. But my family is bigger than that.

my great~grandparents on Father's side

Every one of my eight great-grandparents had a
mother and father.

my great-great-grandparents on Mother's side

That gives me eight great-*great*-grandmothers and
eight great-*great*-grandfathers. And it doesn't stop there.

my great-great-grandparents on Father's side

Each of my eight great-*great*-grandmothers had
a mother and father.

my great~great~great~grandparents on Mother's side

Each of my eight great-*great*-grandfathers had—
WOW! My family never ends.

my great~great~great~grandparents on Father's side

I can make a picture of my family—like this. My family spreads out like a fan. I can't get it all on the page—parents, grandparents, great-grandparents, great-great-grandparents, great-great-great-grandparents, great-great-great-great-grandparents, great-great-great-great-great-grandparents, great-great-great-great-great-great-great-g

There isn't enough paper in this book to make a picture of my family.

Another way to show your family is to start with one of your ancestors. You show him and his wife (or her and her husband) and all their children. Then you show the children's children, and so on until it comes to you. This is called your family tree.

Here is just a part of my family tree. It starts with my great-great-grandfather, Dan Kelly, who had red hair. He and his wife, Martha, had four sons and three daughters.

One of his daughters was my great-grandmother. She and her husband had three sons and three daughters. One of their sons was my grandfather. He and his wife had two sons and two daughters.

One of their sons had red hair. He is my father. My father's brother is my uncle. My father's sisters are my aunts.

I don't know many of the people on my family tree. Most of them were dead before I was born. But I have pictures of some of them.

This is my ancestor Dan Kelly. He had a red beard and red hair. My father says Dan Kelly passed his hair down to us.

The things your ancestors pass down to you are called traits. Red hair is a trait. Brown hair—straight hair—curly hair are traits. The shape of your ears and hands, the color of your eyes, the color of your skin—these are all traits people get from their ancestors.

All the traits from all your ancestors are called your heredity.

Every living thing has heredity. A dog, an elephant, a goldfish—each one gets traits from its ancestors. Even plants have heredity.

For a long time people didn't understand about heredity. They didn't know where traits came from. Some people thought they came only from the mother. Others thought traits came only from the father. Over a hundred years ago Gregor Mendel began to study heredity. He started with plants.

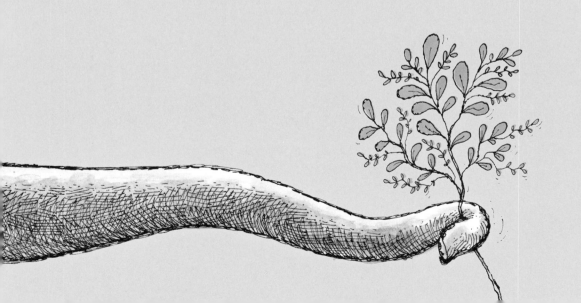

Mendel was a monk. He grew peas in the monastery garden. Some of his pea plants had red flowers. When pollen from a red flower fell on another red flower, seeds were formed. Plants with red flowers grew from these seeds. Mendel also had pea plants with white flowers. Their seeds always grew into plants with white flowers.

24

Mendel decided to try an experiment. He took a little brush and scraped pollen from the red flowers. He brushed this pollen onto the white flowers. This is called cross-pollination.

Mendel cross-pollinated many pea plants in his garden. He carefully saved all the seeds from the cross-pollinated flowers. The next year he planted these seeds and watched them grow into new plants. When flowers came out in these new plants, they were all red. None of these "children" of the red and white plants had white flowers.

When these "children" made seeds, Mendel planted the seeds the next year. The plants that grew from these seeds were the "grandchildren" of his red and white pea plants. Most of the "grandchildren" plants had red flowers. But some of them had white flowers. The white trait had been passed down from the ancestors to some of the "grandchildren" plants.

Mendel repeated this experiment many times. He also studied other traits of his pea plants. He cross-pollinated short plants and tall plants. He kept track of the seeds of hundreds of them. Mendel grew peas for nearly ten years, and he found out some important things about heredity.

He learned that traits come from the ancestors of both the mother and the father. Sometimes these traits—like red hair or long legs—are not seen in the children. But they may show up again in the grandchildren or great-grandchildren.

Hi, Grandpa!

What Mendel learned about pea plants is true of other living things. It is true of some traits in birds and fish, dogs and cats, and other animals. It is true of some traits in people.

People are much harder to study than pea plants. They have many more traits, and their traits are all mixed up. But we can still see some traits from the ancestors in the children and grandchildren.

I get my red hair from my father and my great-great-grandfather. My mother is short, like *her* mother. Perhaps I will be like them. Or I may be tall like my father and his ancestors. I can't tell yet. I don't know all the traits that will come to me from my ancestors. I am still growing.

About the Author

Paul Showers is a retired newspaperman and the author of nearly two dozen books for children. He first became interested in writing for young readers after having watched his own children struggle with the "See, Sally, see" books of the 1950's. His own works—most of them in the Let's-Read-and-Find-Out series—consistently reflect his belief that children's books can be both lively and worthwhile.

Mr. Showers has worked on the Detroit *Free Press,* the New York *Herald Tribune,* the New York *Sunday Mirror*, and, for twenty-nine years, on the Sunday *New York Times*. Born in Sunnyside, Washington, he has an A.B. degree from the University of Michigan.

About the Artist

Don Madden was graduated from the Philadelphia Museum College of Art. A recipient of gold and silver medals at the Philadelphia Art Directors' Club exhibitions, Mr. Madden's work has been selected for reproduction in the *New York Art Directors' Annual*, in the international advertising art publication, *Graphis*, and in the *Society of Illustrators Annual*. The illustrator of many distinguished books for children, he lives with his wife, who is also an artist, and two children in upstate New York.

575.1 Showers, Paul
SHO
     Me and my family
      tree

C-1

DATE			
MAR 13			
NOV 12 1996 318			